PRAISE FOR BECAUSE I CARE

Benjamin Franklin once said, "By failing to plan, you are preparing to fail." Nothing could be more true, especially when considering the details needed for your estate and financial plan. Rena McDonald has created the most comprehensive journal available today for gathering and maintaining crucial personal and financial information needed by family to settle your end-of-life affairs. Don't become a victim of disorganized information. Pick up your copy of, *Because I Care, Estate Planning Journal*, and take the stress and worry out of the process. You will be forever grateful you did.

– Gary C. Laney, Author of *The Power of Strategic Influence* and Serial Entrepreneur

Because I Care: Estate Planning Journal is compiled so well to help anyone handle his/her assets (estate) in planning for the current and future days of life. I read it and found it a wonderful tool, an easy-to-read and understandable guide, and one which covers a breadth of subjects for keeping track of one's holdings.

– Carolyn G. Goodman, Mayor of Las Vegas, Nevada

Rena McDonald has written a helpful workbook for those wishing to make their own death as easy as possible for those they love and leave behind. It will also help focus those thinking about the estate they will leave by clarifying their own thoughts and wishes. Attorneys who write wills and other estate planners can aid clients by recommending this workbook to clients.

– Terrill Pollman, Professor Emerita, Boyd School of Law

You need this book! but more importantly, you need it for every person you care about.
It is difficult to converse with our loved ones about death and dying. And even harder to plan for it.
Rena's easy-to-use workbook is the perfect solution to guide you and your loved ones through the process.
This beautiful & simple workbook provides clear information and gives thoughtful advice. Your loved ones will be grateful.

– Jessica Stokes, Author of *Seeking Clarity in the Labyrinth*

It's brilliant to have all the essential pieces of one's life, legacy, and end-of-life wishes in one remarkable journal, Rena McDonald's *Because I Care,* puts an end to wondering if you've forgotten an important document. Your worries are over as she ties up all the loose ends by thoughtfully guiding you through her process. I especially love the section on Notes To Those I Love, such a compassionate and impactful undertaking. There are so many occasions I could have used this workbook for the people in my life. Rest assured, as an End-of-Life Doula and Bereavement counselor, I will definitely be including this book in my work with others.

– T.J. Marchitelli, Author of *What Not to Do When Your Husband Dies*

Because I Care, should be in every home in America. If you have ever lost a loved one, and then find out they have not left a will or any information on how to settle their estate, you know the stress and overwhelm this causes. While no one wants to think about their passing, we all die, and leaving a guide for your family is the most compassionate and helpful thing you can do.

How I wish I had a copy of this book to work on with my mom before she passed. I wonder to this day if I did what she would have wanted.

I've seen families changed forever by a relative who left no will or instructions. All things were left to be decided by a spouse or partner, putting immense pressure on them to "get it right" and I have seen families torn apart by this forever. It is a burden I would not want to leave anyone! Especially someone I love.

Loving your family includes leaving a plan. Please, don't add to your loved one's grief by leaving them a mess. Make time to leave a plan and details to help them easily and quickly settle their estate while they suffer your loss.

Rena gives us nothing to think about and all the prompts we could need, from basic info like debts, insurance, and dependents, to more complicated details like funeral/memorial plans, who gets what, and the combo to the safe and social media passwords. This comprehensive guide leaves little to the imagination and will allow your wishes to be carried out to a "T", making it easier for loved ones to navigate while grieving.

Your last act of love to your surviving loved ones is to complete this book. Please get a copy for all the adults in your family. It will be a gift of much-needed help after you are gone.

– Judy Granlee Gates, Author of *Bigger Living, Smaller Space*

An Estate Planning Journal

Attorney,
Rena McDonald

Red Thread Publishing LLC. 2023
Write to info@redthreadbooks.com if you are interested in publishing with Red Thread Publishing. Learn more about publications or foreign rights acquisitions of our catalog of books: **www.redthreadbooks.com**

Paperback ISBN: 978-1-955683-45-6
Ebook ISBN: 978-1-955683-46-3

Cover Design: Sierra Melcher

TABLE OF CONTENTS

1. Introduction

1. INTRODUCTION

This book is a valuable tool that was created for you to leave to your loved ones. In our many years of creating estate plans, we are often contacted by the grieving loved one of someone recently departed. They are dealing with loss and having to deal with these important business and paperwork issues is often too much. By taking the time to document your crucial personal information, you will help your loved ones by giving them peace of mind during a very difficult time. This book creates an all-in-one tool for all of your most valuable Information. Fill it out in the first person and allow it to speak for you to your loved ones. We suggest you review it once a year to make sure it is up to date. Also share it with the people who will be in charge of helping.

2. How to use this book

and who needs it

2. HOW TO USE THIS BOOK

This book is for two distinct groups of people.
The first is for the persons who are filling it out. You are leaving this Information for the people you love. You might be doing this as part of creating or updating your estate plan. Or maybe you just saw it and thought it would work for you. Regardless of how this book got in your hands, take the time to fill it out. As with most things, it may be easier to do a little at a time. Don't feel like you have to complete it all at once but do come back to it and complete it. Every piece of Information you give your loved one saves them more time and effort. Remember why you are filling this out, ***because you care.***

The second group is for the ones we leave behind. If you are reviewing this book after your loved one has passed, this book is intended to help you navigate the loss of your loved one. It should contain all pertinent Information about your loved one because they cared enough about you to write it down. Ideally, the one filling out this document should review each section with their loved ones and make sure that they know where to access it.

I have been an attorney since 2004 and have dealt with countless estates and probate matters. Without such a document, the biggest issue that clients ran into was something I was unable to help them with-lack of information.

The question is always, "Now what?" The first thing the loved one has to do after someone passes is to get a handle on what they left behind. You have to know the assets, where they are, and how to access them. You also need to know how to access the debts and obligations of an estate before you can start to resolve them. That means if your parent passes or becomes incapacitated, you have to know how to access their Information.

Once you have this Information, you have an obligation to make sure that the assets get passed to the heirs or beneficiaries. That can be done in various ways depending upon the type of estate you are dealing with, whether it is a trust, or a will, etc. This will vary depending upon the state or country you live in. But without knowing what you are dealing with, you have no clarity about how to help.

In a recent case, my client's ailing mother quickly became ill and was unable to care for herself. My client had no idea what her mother owned or owed. It took almost a year to get that all worked out. In the meantime, my client had to pay out of pocket to make sure everything was handled for her mother, all while she was being harassed by creditors. Had her mother planned ahead and passed the relevant information on to her daughter, all that stress and expense could have been prevented.

This case is in sharp contrast to another client who knew she was close to death and had the time to go over all of these issues and concerns with her spouse. After she passed, her spouse had no added difficulty dealing with the legal and financial ramifications. Everything was easily transferred and dealt with. Unfortunately, life does not always give us the time to plan and pass this Information on when it is necessary. Taking time now can make sure all relevant data is available when needed.

Every state or country is different as to time periods and specifics, but you have limited periods of time in which to act to protect yourself and the estate after someone passes. If you don't even know what debt a person has and are awaiting responses, you could miss those dates.

In the past, the best advice I could give was to run a credit report or wait for mail to come in. But now in the digital age with online accounts, invoices and statements, even that may not give you an entire picture of what is going on. Also, none of that gives you any indication of assets. You can request a copy of a tax return, but that could take months to years to receive. Having a centralized place to access this Information is invaluable to the people you care about.

A valid will, will make sure that your assets go to the people you love. Having a valid trust can potentially protect your assets from going into probate or to creditors. Probate is expensive, and a trust can protect your heirs from having to deal with that. It is also important to make sure you have the proper power of attorney or POA documents. POAs protect you while you are alive but can't make decisions for you. While you are able, you should make sure you take the time to name someone you trust who understands your wishes.

This planner is not intended to be legal advice and does not replace a valid will, trust or estate plan. You should consult with a licensed attorney regarding any legal questions or concerns you may have. This book is for Informational purposes only.

more notes

JAN	FEB	MAR	APR	MAY	JUN	JUL	AUG	SEP	OCT	NOV	DEC

1 2 3 4 5 6 7 8 9 10 11 12 13 14 15 16 17 18 19 20 21 22 23 24 25 26 27 28 29 30 31

3. Security

3. SECURITY

This book will become a wealth of personal and confidential Information. You want to make sure this Information is not made public and only your most trusted loved ones have access to it. I suggest you keep it in a secured location or safe. You can protect your online information using a password protection application to keep and update your passwords. But that does not mean you should only look at this book once. This information changes regularly and so should the information you leave herein. My recommendation would be that you review it yearly to confirm everything is up to date. January is a good time to look at it as you are looking forward to the new year. Put it on your calendar and make a date with yourself. It will just take a few moments but could mean hours, weeks, or years of agonizing time for your loved ones.

Also, don't forget to notify the proper authorities of the passing of a loved one. A sad example of such an oversight is when a client of ours lost a young daughter. As if that wasn't traumatic enough, several years later they received notice from the IRS that their daughter owed taxes for a recent job. Someone had stolen the child's social security number and was working illegally under that number. The clients then had to work with the IRS, repeatedly having to advise that the child had passed. It took several years to resolve and was a horrific reminder of their loss.

more notes

JAN	FEB	MAR	APR	MAY	JUN	JUL	AUG	SEP	OCT	NOV	DEC

1 2 3 4 5 6 7 8 9 10 11 12 13 14 15 16 17 18 19 20 21 22 23 24 25 26 27 28 29 30 31

4. Communication

4. COMMUNICATION

Don't forget to give access to this safe spot where you keep this book to the ones you want to use this Information. It is great to have this book and fill it out, but your loved ones need to know it exists and how to access it or it is useless.

While conversations about these matters can be difficult, they are very important. When my grandmother found out she had cancer, we discussed her wishes at length. While they were hard conversations, I got to know her better in those last few months than I had my entire life. I am so thankful for those conversations and the openness she shared with me. It was a gift and I know that those discussions helped make sure her wishes were fulfilled.

Fill out every section as fully as possible, protect it, don't forget to come back to revise it frequently, and make sure someone knows how to access it.

more notes

JAN	FEB	MAR	APR	MAY	JUN	JUL	AUG	SEP	OCT	NOV	DEC

1 2 3 4 5 6 7 8 9 10 11 12 13 14 15 16 17 18 19 20 21 22 23 24 25 26 27 28 29 30 31

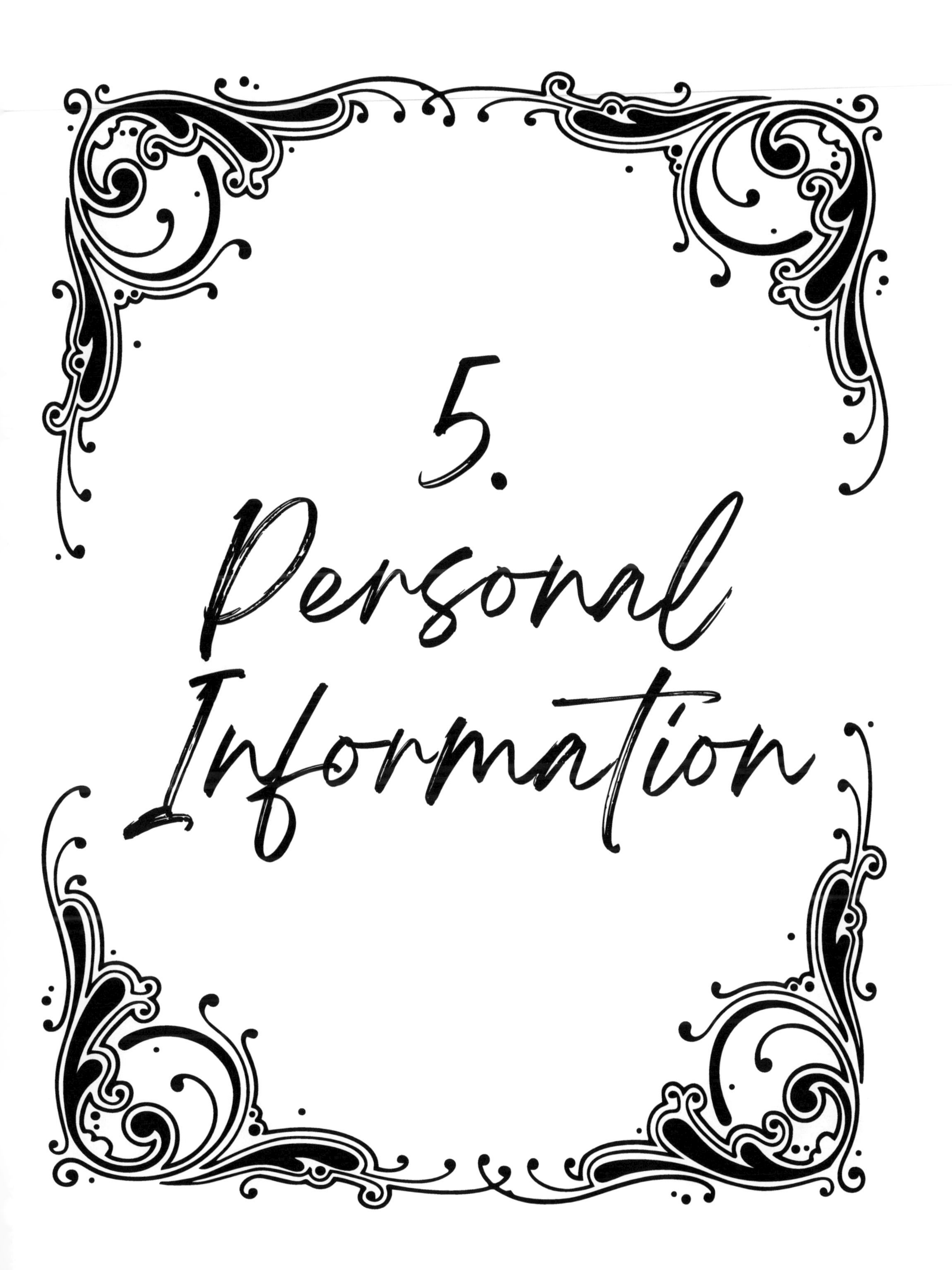

5. Personal Information

5. PERSONAL INFORMATION

While this is basic Information, it is important to make sure the people taking care of your estate are aware of it. They will need to notify the proper channels, family members, etc. A client of ours did not know who the members of the deceased family were or if they were alive. They had to do extensive research that was both expensive and time-consuming. It left very little in the estate and I am sure the person who passed would rather those funds went to their heirs than to the personal investigator they had to hire to get that Information.

Personal Information

Legal Name

Alias/Maiden Name

Address

Phone

Mobile Numbers

Cell Phone Provider

Cell Phone Password

Password Protection Manager

Username

Password/Pin

Social Security Number

Birthplace

Marital Status

Occupation

Military Service

Notes:

Spouse Information

Alias/Maiden Name

Address

Phone

Mobile Numbers

Social Security number

Birthplace

Notes:

Children Information

Child's Name

Alias/Maiden Name

Address

Phone

Mobile Numbers

Social Security Number

Birthplace

Notes:

Child's Name

Alias/Maiden Name

Address

Phone

Mobile Numbers

Social Security Number

Birthplace

Notes:

Child's Name

Alias/Maiden Name

Address

Phone

Mobile Numbers

Social Security Number

Birthplace

Notes:

Children: Information

Child's Name

Alias/Maiden Name

Address

Phone

Mobile Numbers

Social Security Number

Birthplace

Notes:

Child's Name

Alias/Maiden Name

Address

Phone

Mobile Numbers

Social Security Number

Birthplace

Notes:

Child's Name

Alias/Maiden Name

Address

Phone

Mobile Numbers

Social Security Number

Birthplace

Notes:

Grandchildren

Grandchild's Name ______________________

Alias/Maiden Name ______________________

Address ______________________

Phone ______________________

Mobile Numbers ______________________

Social Security Number ______________________

Birthplace ______________________

Notes:

Grandchild's Name ______________________

Alias/Maiden Name ______________________

Address ______________________

Phone ______________________

Mobile Numbers ______________________

Social Security Number ______________________

Birthplace ______________________

Notes:

Grandchildren (Cont.)

Grandchild's Name ____________________

Alias/Maiden Name ____________________

Address ____________________

Phone ____________________

Mobile Numbers ____________________

Social Security Number ____________________

Birthplace ____________________

Notes:

Grandchild's Name ____________________

Alias/Maiden Name ____________________

Address ____________________

Phone ____________________

Mobile Numbers ____________________

Social Security Number ____________________

Birthplace ____________________

Notes:

Grandchildren (Cont.)

Grandchild's Name

Alias/Maiden Name

Address

Phone

Mobile Numbers

Social Security Number

Birthplace

Notes:

Grandchild's Name

Alias/Maiden Name

Address

Phone

Mobile Numbers

Social Security Number

Birthplace

Notes:

Former Spouse(s)

Former Spouse's Name ______

Alias/Maiden Name ______

Address ______

Phone ______

Mobile Numbers ______

Social Security Number ______

Birthplace ______

Notes:

Former Spouse's Name ______

Alias/Maiden Name ______

Address ______

Phone ______

Mobile Numbers ______

Social Security Number ______

Birthplace ______

Notes:

Siblings

Sibling's Name ______

Alias/Maiden Name ______

Address ______

Phone ______

Mobile Numbers ______

Social Security Number ______

Birthplace ______

Notes:

Sibling's Name ______

Alias/Maiden Name ______

Address ______

Phone ______

Mobile Numbers ______

Social Security Number ______

Birthplace ______

Notes:

Siblings

Sibling's Name

Alias/Maiden Name

Address

Phone

Mobile Numbers

Social Security Number

Birthplace

Notes:

Sibling's Name

Alias/Maiden Name

Address

Phone

Mobile Numbers

Social Security Number

Birthplace

Notes:

Parents

Father's Name

Alias

Address

Phone

Mobile Numbers

Social Security Number

Father's birthplace

Notes:

Mother's Name

Alias/Maiden Name

Address

Phone

Mobile Numbers

Social Security Number

Mother's birthplace

Notes:

Personal Information

Extended Family

Name

Relationship

Alias/Maiden Name

Address

Phone

Mobile Numbers

Social Security Number

Birthplace

Notes:

Name

Relationship

Alias/Maiden Name

Address

Phone

Mobile Numbers

Social Security Number

Birthplace

Notes:

Extended Family (Cont.)

Name

Relationship

Alias/Maiden Name

Address

Phone

Mobile Numbers

Social Security Number

Birthplace

Notes:

Name

Relationship

Alias/Maiden Name

Address

Phone

Mobile Numbers

Social Security Number

Birthplace

Notes:

more notes

JAN	FEB	MAR	APR	MAY	JUN	JUL	AUG	SEP	OCT	NOV	DEC

1 2 3 4 5 6 7 8 9 10 11 12 13 14 15 16 17 18 19 20 21 22 23 24 25 26 27 28 29 30 31

6. Important People to Contact

6. IMPORTANT PEOPLE TO CONTACT

Don't forget to include people that aren't beneficiaries but that you know would want to be aware that you passed. Longtime friends, employers, etc.

contacts

Name & Address | **Contact Numbers**

Name ____________________ Relationship ____________________
____________________ Cellphone ____________________
____________________ Home ____________________
____________________ E-mail ____________________

Name ____________________ Relationship ____________________
____________________ Cellphone ____________________
____________________ Home ____________________
____________________ E-mail ____________________

Name ____________________ Relationship ____________________
____________________ Cellphone ____________________
____________________ Home ____________________
____________________ E-mail ____________________

Name ____________________ Relationship ____________________
____________________ Cellphone ____________________
____________________ Home ____________________
____________________ E-mail ____________________

6. IMPORTANT PEOPLE TO CONTACT

Name & Address | **Contact Numbers**

Name ____________________ Relationship ____________________
____________________ Cellphone ____________________
____________________ Home ____________________
____________________ E-mail ____________________

Name ____________________ Relationship ____________________
____________________ Cellphone ____________________
____________________ Home ____________________
____________________ E-mail ____________________

Name ____________________ Relationship ____________________
____________________ Cellphone ____________________
____________________ Home ____________________
____________________ E-mail ____________________

Name ____________________ Relationship ____________________
____________________ Cellphone ____________________
____________________ Home ____________________
____________________ E-mail ____________________

Name ____________________ Relationship ____________________
____________________ Cellphone ____________________
____________________ Home ____________________
____________________ E-mail ____________________

more notes

JAN	FEB	MAR	APR	MAY	JUN	JUL	AUG	SEP	OCT	NOV	DEC

1 2 3 4 5 6 7 8 9 10 11 12 13 14 15 16 17 18 19 20 21 22 23 24 25 26 27 28 29 30 31

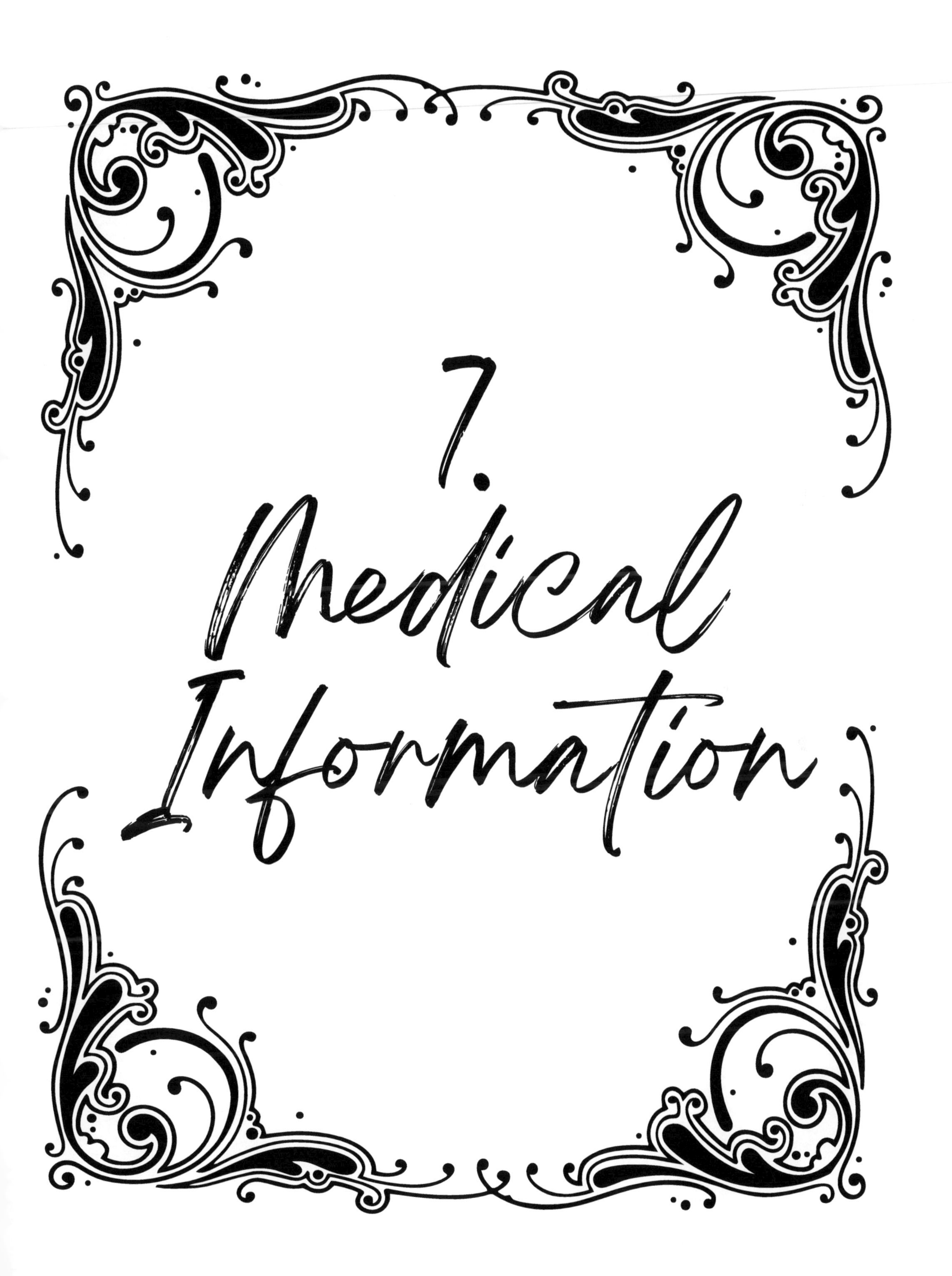

7. Medical Information

7. MEDICAL INFORMATION

Too often our loved ones lose the capacity to speak for themselves. This is especially true as we continue to live longer with diminished mental faculties. You want to make sure that your loved ones are aware of your doctors and medicines so that they can ensure you continue to receive the medical treatment you need.

Medical Information

Medical POA documents

Who is your medical POA

Where is your POA

DNR

Organ Donor

Blood type

Allergies

Medical conditions

Medications

Health Insurance

Where is the health insurance card

Physicians

Primary Care

Preferred pharmacy

Insurance Information

Insurance #1

Provider:

Policy number:

Emergency Helpline:

Registered Member:

Important Notes

Insurance #2

Provider:

Policy number:

Emergency Helpline:

Registered Member:

Important Notes

7. MEDICAL INFORMATION

Name:

Age :

Blood Type:

Primary Doctor:

Allergies:

Chronic Conditions:

Medical History

DATE	ILLNESS / SURGERIES	DOCTOR / HOSPITAL

Medical contacts

NAME :
SPECIALTIES :
ADDRESS :
PHONE :
EMAIL :
NOTES :

NAME :
SPECIALTIES :
ADDRESS :
PHONE :
EMAIL :
NOTES :

NAME :
SPECIALTIES :
ADDRESS :
PHONE :
EMAIL :
NOTES :

NAME :
SPECIALTIES :
ADDRESS :
PHONE :
EMAIL :
NOTES :

more notes

JAN	FEB	MAR	APR	MAY	JUN	JUL	AUG	SEP	OCT	NOV	DEC

1 2 3 4 5 6 7 8 9 10 11 12 13 14 15 16 17 18 19 20 21 22 23 24 25 26 27 28 29 30 31

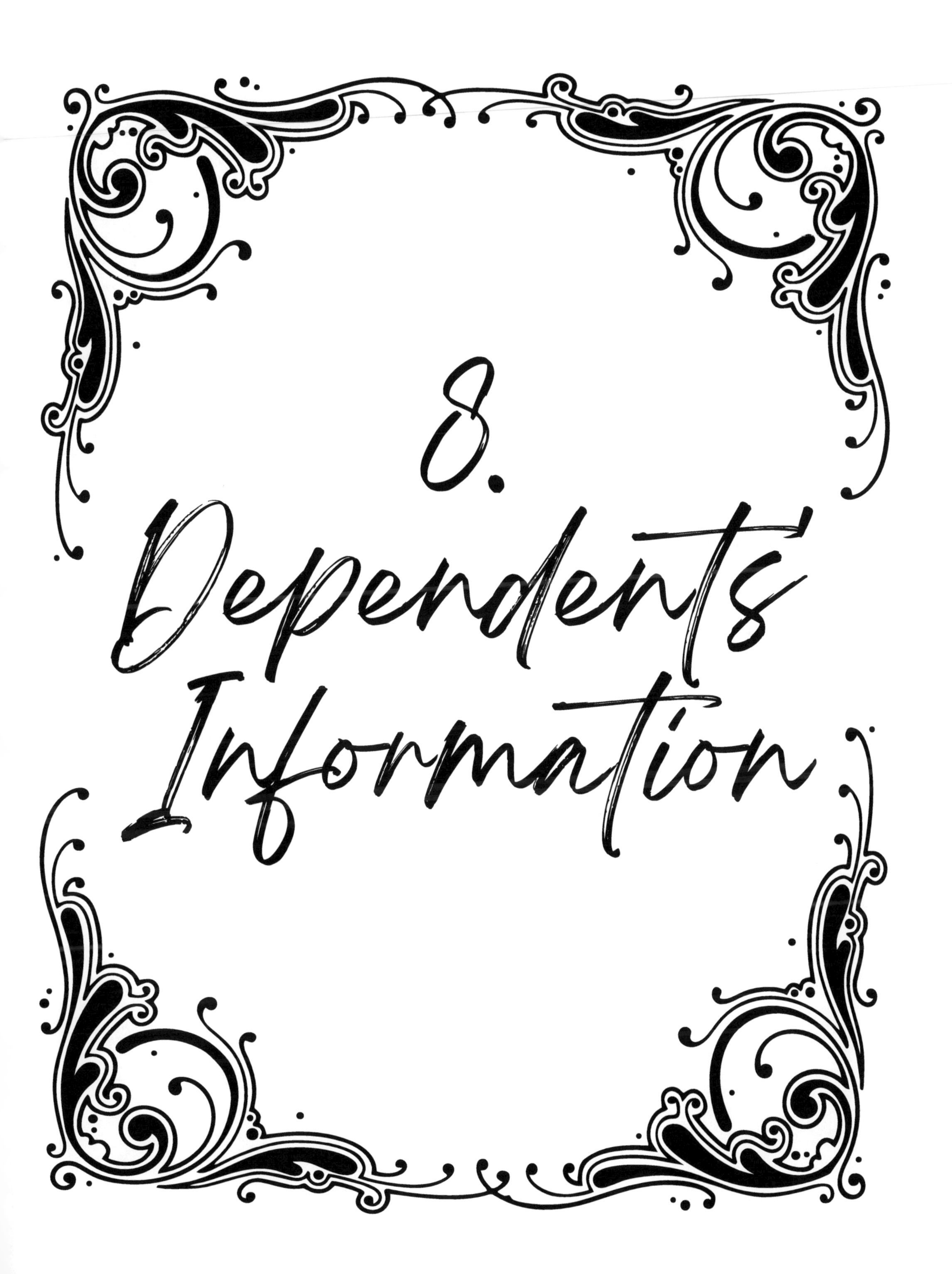

8. Dependents' Information

8. DEPENDENTS' INFORMATION

As a mother, I know how important this section is. I often see situations where only one parent is aware of this Information and if they pass, the other parent is scrambling to try to figure this out. Leave that Information here so that the remaining parent can confidently act to protect your dependents.

Dependents

Name

Relationship

Contact Information

Birth date and Place

Personal Information SS #

Personal Insurance

Caregiving, custody, or guardianship Information

Health Information

Allergies

Primary Care Physicians

Social Security Number

Financial Information

Bank accounts

Insurance Policies

Notes

Dependents

Name

Relationship

Contact Information

Birth date and Place

Personal Information SS #

Personal Insurance

Caregiving, custody, or guardianship Information

Health Information

Allergies

Primary Care Physicians

Social Security Number

Financial Information

Bank accounts

Insurance Policies

Notes

Dependents

Name

Relationship

Contact Information

Birth date and Place

Personal Information SS #

Personal Insurance

Caregiving, custody, or guardianship Information

Health Information

Allergies

Primary Care Physicians

Social Security Number

Financial Information

Bank accounts

Insurance Policies

Notes

Dependents

Name

Relationship

Contact Information

Birth date and Place

Personal Information SS #

Personal Insurance

Caregiving, custody, or guardianship Information

Health Information

Allergies

Primary Care Physicians

Social Security Number

Financial Information

Bank accounts

Insurance Policies

Notes

more notes

JAN	FEB	MAR	APR	MAY	JUN	JUL	AUG	SEP	OCT	NOV	DEC

1 2 3 4 5 6 7 8 9 10 11 12 13 14 15 16 17 18 19 20 21 22 23 24 25 26 27 28 29 30 31

9. Financial

9. FINANCIAL INFORMATION

This is one of the most important sections. This Information is not only for when you pass but also for when you can no longer speak for yourself under the designation of a financial Power of Attorney (POA). You want to make sure someone knows this Information so that they can help you.

Another client had an issue with a parent's vehicle, and it took six months to figure out who the loan for the vehicle was with and he couldn't make a payment during that time. So, by the time he figured it out, the car was being repossessed. Make sure someone knows this critical Information so they can make sure the lights stay on and the assets are preserved.

Powers of Attorney ____________________

Who is in charge ____________________

Where is the document ____________________

What do you want done? ____________________

Banks ____________________

Account Number ____________________

Online user ID ____________________

Password ____________________

Debit card number ____________________

Username ____________________

Password/Pin ____________________

Account Number ____________________

Online user ID ____________________

Password/Pin ____________________

Notes ____________________

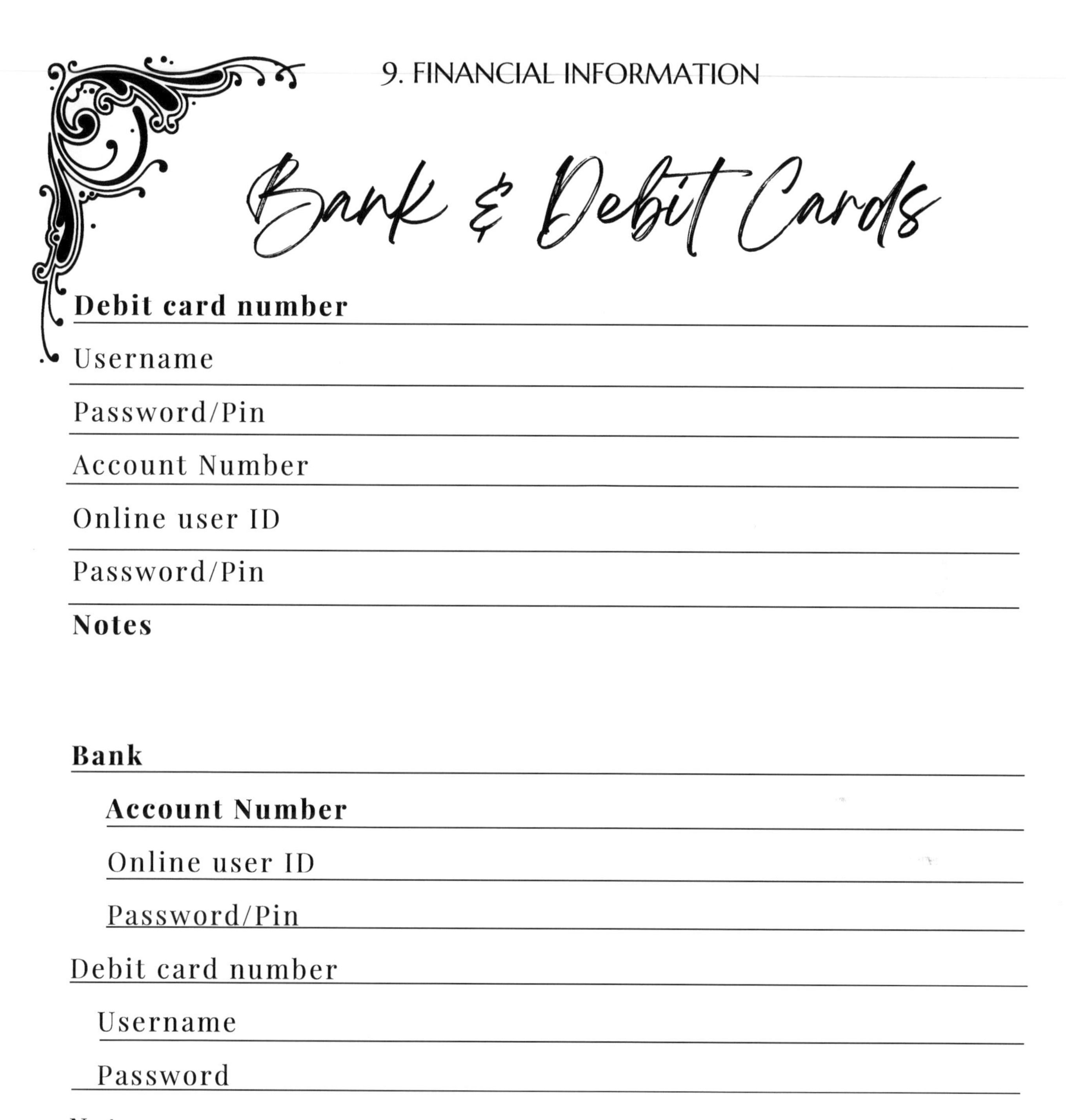

Bank & Debit Cards

Debit card number

Username

Password/Pin

Account Number

Online user ID

Password/Pin

Notes

Bank

Account Number

Online user ID

Password/Pin

Debit card number

Username

Password

Notes:

Bank ____________________

Account Number ____________________

Online user ID ____________________

Password ____________________

Debit card number ____________________

Username ____________________

Password/Pin ____________________

Notes

Bank ____________________

Account Number ____________________

Online user ID ____________________

Password ____________________

Debit card number ____________________

Username ____________________

Password/Pin ____________________

Notes

Financial Information

Bank ___

Account Number ___

Online user ID ___

Password ___

Debit card number ___

Username ___

Password/Pin ___

Notes

Bank ___

Account Number ___

Online user ID ___

Password ___

Debit card number ___

Username ___

Password/Pin ___

Notes

Financial Information

Bank ______

Account Number ______

Online user ID ______

Password ______

Debit card number ______

Username ______

Password/Pin ______

Notes

Bank ______

Account Number ______

Online user ID ______

Password ______

Debit card number ______

Username ______

Password/Pin ______

Notes

Bank ______

Account Number ______

Online user ID ______

Password ______

Debit card number ______

Username ______

Password/Pin ______

Notes

Credit Cards

Credit Card Information

Type/Name

Account Number

Username

Password/Pin

Phone Number

Notes

Type/Name

Account Number

Username

Password/Pin

Phone Number

Notes

Type/Name

Account Number

Username

Password/Pin

Phone Number

Notes

Store Credit Cards

Store Credit Card Information

Type/Name

Account Number

Username

Password/Pin

Phone Number

Notes

Type/Name

Account Number

Username

Password/Pin

Phone Number

Notes

Type/Name

Account Number

Username

Password/Pin

Phone Number

Notes

Investments

Investments, Stocks, Bonds, Retirement, Etc.

Description/Type/Name

Account Number

Phone Number

Username

Password

Notes

Description/Type/Name

Account Number

Phone Number

Username

Password

Notes

Description/Type/Name

Account Number

Phone Number

Username

Password

Notes

Investments

Investments, Stocks, Bonds, Retirement, Etc.

Description/Type/Name

Account Number

Phone Number

Username

Password

Notes

Description/Type/Name

Account Number

Phone Number

Username

Password

Notes

Description/Type/Name

Account Number

Phone Number

Username

Password

Notes

Other Accounts

Rewards, Frequent Flyer, Etc.

Description/Type/Name

Account Number

Phone Number

Username

Password/Pin

Notes

Description/Type/Name

Account Number

Phone Number

Username

Password

Notes

Description/Type/Name

Account Number

Phone Number

Username

Password

Notes

Tax Information

Tax Information

Where is this information

Online Tax Account

Description

Account Number

Contact

Username

Password

Notes

Safe Deposit

Safe Deposit Account

Bank and Location

Number

Location of Safe Deposit Key

Contents

Notes

Safe Deposit Account

Bank and Location

Number

Location of Safe Deposit Key

Contents

Notes

more notes

JAN	FEB	MAR	APR	MAY	JUN	JUL	AUG	SEP	OCT	NOV	DEC

1 2 3 4 5 6 7 8 9 10 11 12 13 14 15 16 17 18 19 20 21 22 23 24 25 26 27 28 29 30 31

10. Debt

Debt

Debt

Mortgage

Lender Information

Account Number

Username

Password

Notes

Car Information

Lender Information

Account Number

Username

Password

Notes

Student Loan

Lender Information

Account Number

Username

Password

Notes

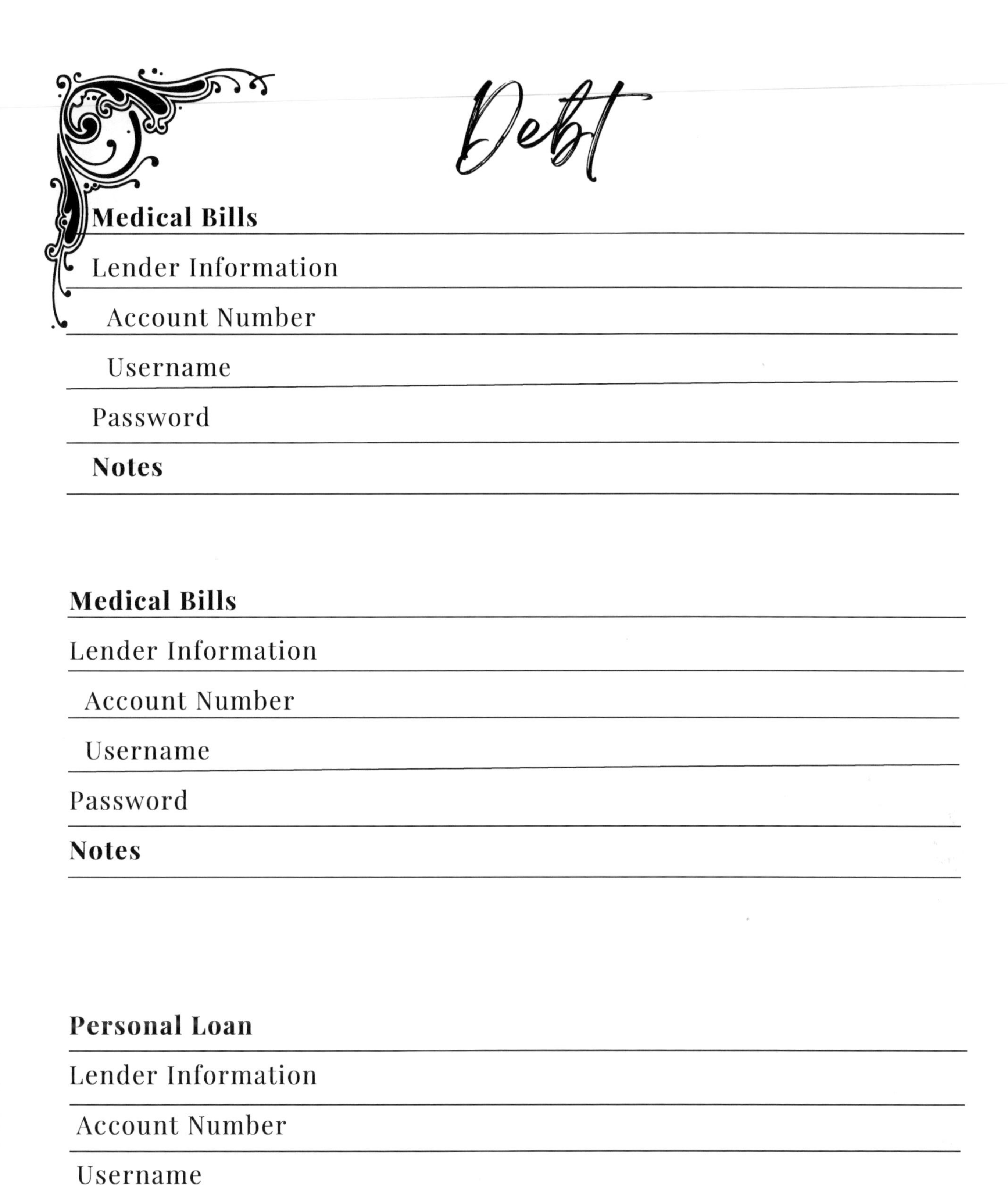

Debt

Medical Bills

Lender Information

Account Number

Username

Password

Notes

Medical Bills

Lender Information

Account Number

Username

Password

Notes

Personal Loan

Lender Information

Account Number

Username

Password

Notes

Debt

Judgments/Lawsuits

Contact Information

Account Number

Notes

Other Debt

Lender Information

Account Number

Username

Password

Notes

Assets Owed to me

Contact

Notes

DEBT TRACKER

Debt :

Contact:

Account:

User name/ Password:

DATE	NOTES	BALANCE

Debt :

Contact:

Account:

User name/ Password:

DATE	NOTES	BALANCE

Debt :

Contact:

Account:

User name/ Password:

DATE	NOTES	BALANCE

Debt :

Contact:

Account:

User name/ Password:

DATE	NOTES	BALANCE

more notes

JAN	FEB	MAR	APR	MAY	JUN	JUL	AUG	SEP	OCT	NOV	DEC

1 2 3 4 5 6 7 8 9 10 11 12 13 14 15 16 17 18 19 20 21 22 23 24 25 26 27 28 29 30 31

II. Business

11. BUSINESS

Having a business succession plan is vital to every business. Many business owners often wait to figure this out assuming a family member will take up ownership after they have passed. Especially when you have employees counting on you, leaving your business succession up in the air is never a good idea. Countless companies close because the owner did not take the time to make this important arrangement ahead of time. Even if the business is valuable, a few months of inoperability will dramatically decrease the clients and value for the people you want to leave it to. Figure out who is going to run it if you can and make sure they agree and pass on the Information they need so they can keep the doors open.

Business Name

Location

Contact Information

Landlord

Location of keys

Manager Information

Employees Contact Information

Accountant Information

Bookkeeper Information

Attorney Information

Website Information

Server Information

Critical Dates

Business Licenses

Domain registration renewals

Hosting renewals

Line of Business contract expiration/ due dates

Renewal/auto renewals

Vendor payments

Business Social Media Sites

Business Insurance Information

Bank Account Information

Account Number

Online user ID

Password

Notes

Debit card number

Username

Password

Notes

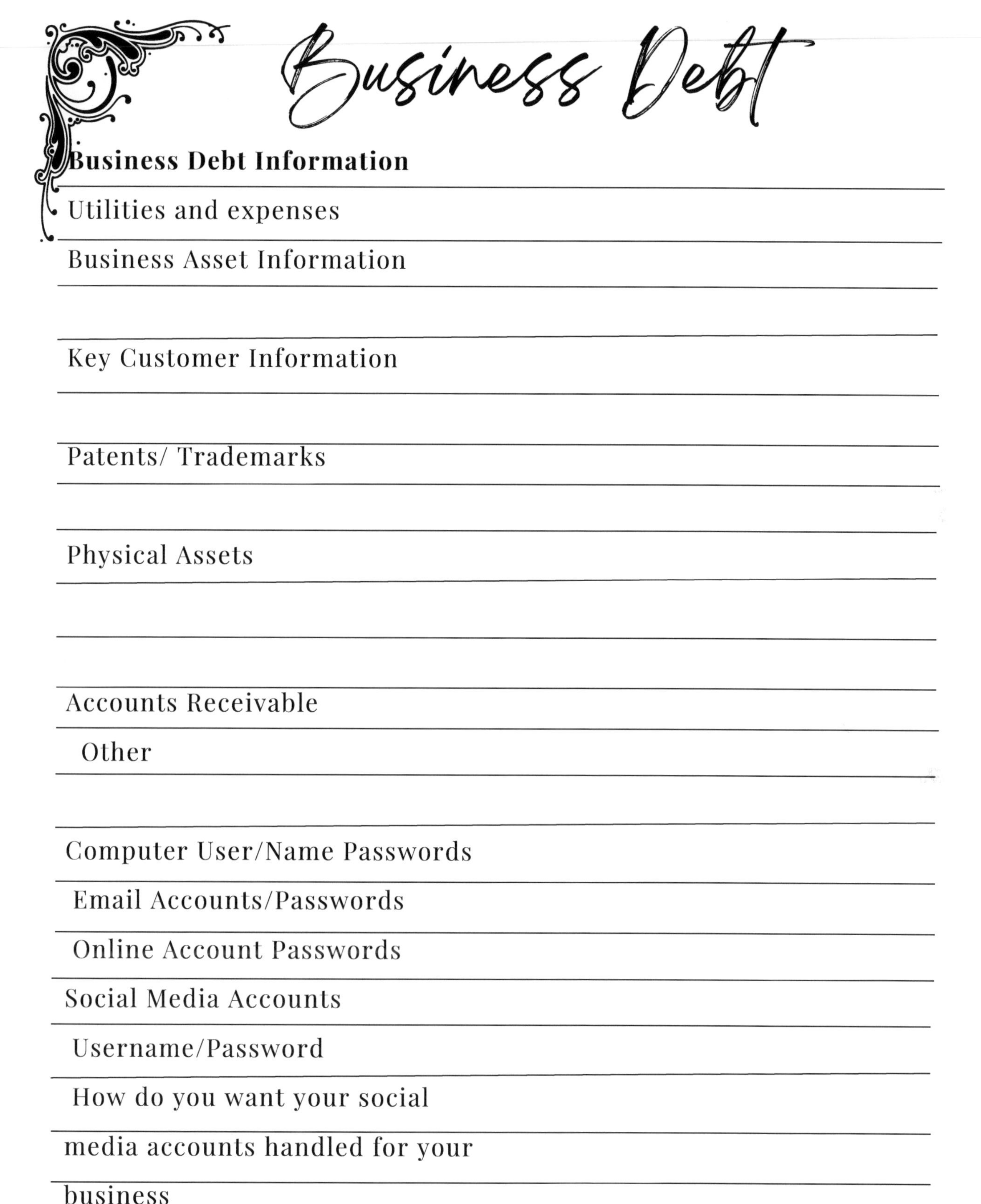

Business Debt

Business Debt Information

Utilities and expenses

Business Asset Information

Key Customer Information

Patents/ Trademarks

Physical Assets

Accounts Receivable

Other

Computer User/Name Passwords

Email Accounts/Passwords

Online Account Passwords

Social Media Accounts

Username/Password

How do you want your social media accounts handled for your business

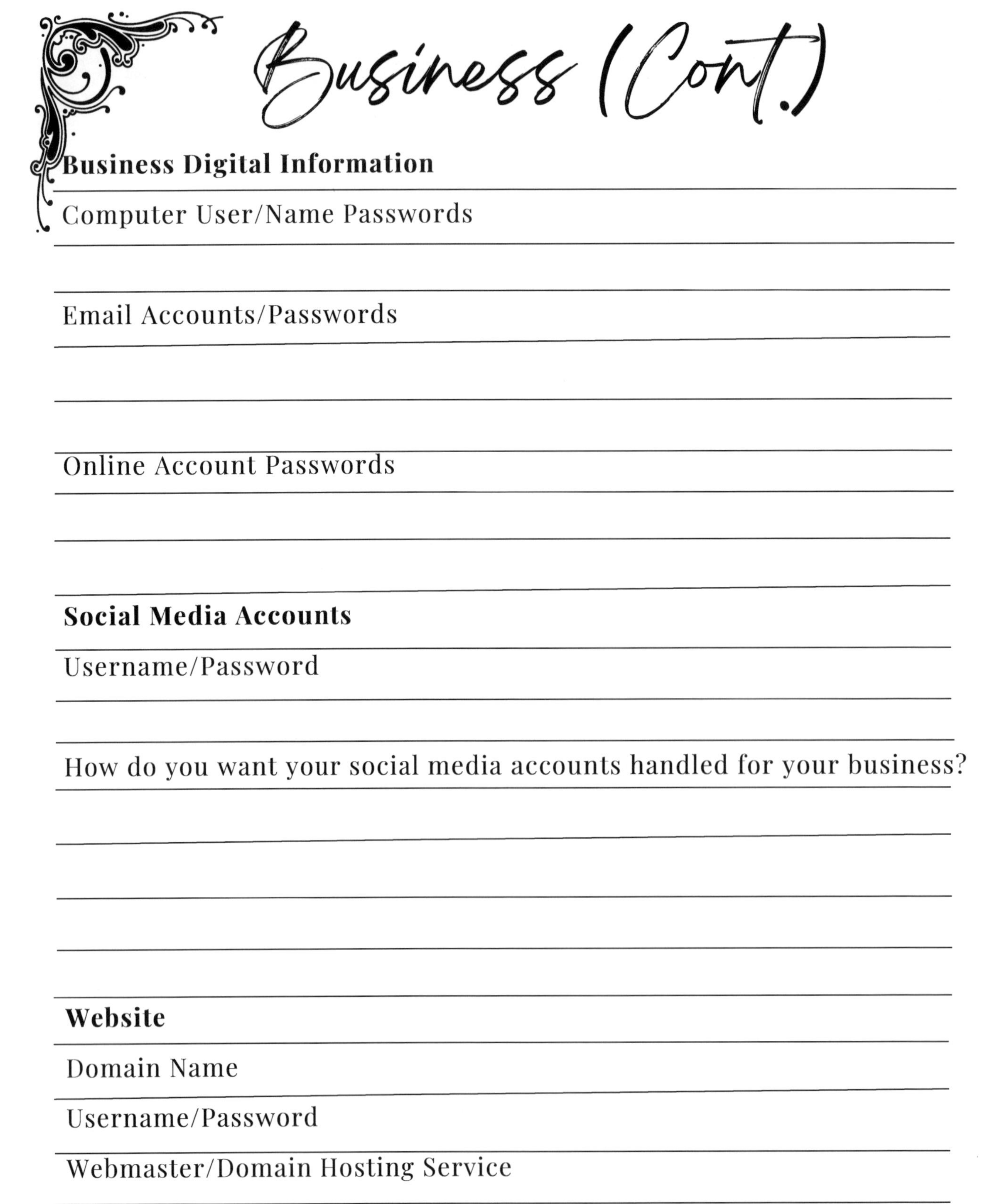

Business (Cont.)

Business Digital Information

Computer User/Name Passwords

Email Accounts/Passwords

Online Account Passwords

Social Media Accounts

Username/Password

How do you want your social media accounts handled for your business?

Website

Domain Name

Username/Password

Webmaster/Domain Hosting Service

more notes

JAN	FEB	MAR	APR	MAY	JUN	JUL	AUG	SEP	OCT	NOV	DEC

1 2 3 4 5 6 7 8 9 10 11 12 13 14 15 16 17 18 19 20 21 22 23 24 25 26 27 28 29 30 31

12. Who Gets What

12. WHO GETS WHAT

I often have clients ask me how they should divide up their assets and the truth is, that is totally up to you. If you decide you prefer one child over another or don't want your sister to get mom's china, that is your choice. What I do care about is making sure you include that Information into your estate and this book. I want to make sure that whoever is managing your estate knows your wishes and exactly what they are supposed to do. If not, you are asking for family squabbles, Court intervention and additional attorneys fees. Write it down!

Who Gets What

Life Insurance

Contact Information

Type of policy and number

Amount

Beneficiary

Where is the document

Notes

Social Security

Name

Account Number

Contact Information

Where is the document

Notes

Retirement Accounts

Contact Information

Type of policy and number

Amount

Beneficiary

Where is the document

Notes

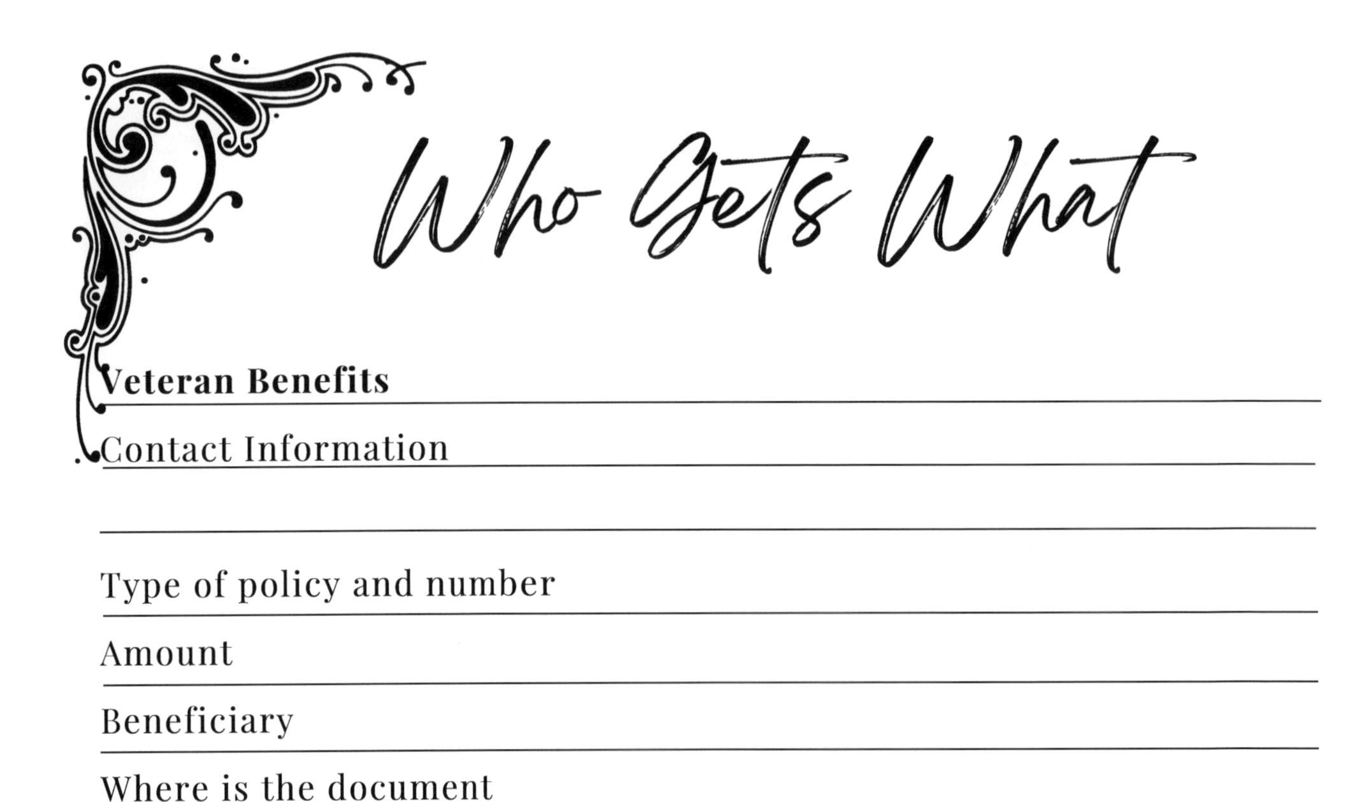

Veteran Benefits

Contact Information

Type of policy and number

Amount

Beneficiary

Where is the document

Who Gets What

Item	Recipient

12. WHO GETS WHAT

MY STUFF

MONTH: YEAR:

Item	Give to

more notes

JAN	FEB	MAR	APR	MAY	JUN	JUL	AUG	SEP	OCT	NOV	DEC

1 2 3 4 5 6 7 8 9 10 11 12 13 14 15 16 17 18 19 20 21 22 23 24 25 26 27 28 29 30 31

B.
Accounts
and
Passwords

PASSWORD TRACKER

COMPUTER:
USERNAME:
PASSWORD:
NOTES:

PHONE:
USERNAME:
PASSWORD:
NOTES:

EMAIL:
USERNAME:
PASSWORD:
NOTES:

EMAIL:
USERNAME:
PASSWORD:
NOTES:

SOCIAL MEDIA:
USERNAME:
PASSWORD:
NOTES:

SOCIAL MEDIA:
USERNAME:
PASSWORD:
NOTES:

WEBSITE:
USERNAME:
PASSWORD:
WEBMASTER/HOSTING:

WEBSITE:
USERNAME:
PASSWORD:
WEBMASTER/HOSTING:

PASSWORD TRACKER

WEBSITE:
USERNAME:
PASSWORD:
NOTES:

WEBSITE:
USERNAME:
PASSWORD:
NOTES:

WEBSITE:
USERNAME:
PASSWORD:
NOTES:

WEBSITE:
USERNAME:
PASSWORD:
NOTES:

WEBSITE:
USERNAME:
PASSWORD:
NOTES:

WEBSITE:
USERNAME:
PASSWORD:
NOTES:

WEBSITE:
USERNAME:
PASSWORD:
NOTES:

WEBSITE:
USERNAME:
PASSWORD:
NOTES:

PASSWORD TRACKER

WEBSITE:
USERNAME:
PASSWORD:
NOTES:

WEBSITE:
USERNAME:
PASSWORD:
NOTES:

WEBSITE:
USERNAME:
PASSWORD:
NOTES:

WEBSITE:
USERNAME:
PASSWORD:
NOTES:

WEBSITE:
USERNAME:
PASSWORD:
NOTES:

WEBSITE:
USERNAME:
PASSWORD:
NOTES:

WEBSITE:
USERNAME:
PASSWORD:
NOTES:

WEBSITE:
USERNAME:
PASSWORD:
NOTES:

more notes

JAN	FEB	MAR	APR	MAY	JUN	JUL	AUG	SEP	OCT	NOV	DEC

1 2 3 4 5 6 7 8 9 10 11 12 13 14 15 16 17 18 19 20 21 22 23 24 25 26 27 28 29 30 31

14. Pets' Information

14. PETS' INFORMATION

To assure that your pets are cared for, make sure someone is willing to take that responsibility. All too often someone passes and their pets are given to a shelter, too old to be adopted, and are thus euthanized. You can create a pet trust which specifically gives a financial gift to the parties that take your pets, giving them a financial incentive. Just have that conversation beforehand.

Pet Name ______________________________

Description/Breed/Age ______________________________

License Information ______________________________

Vet Information ______________________________

Health Information ______________________________

Instructions for ___ who will take care of my pet

____

14. PETS' INFORMATION

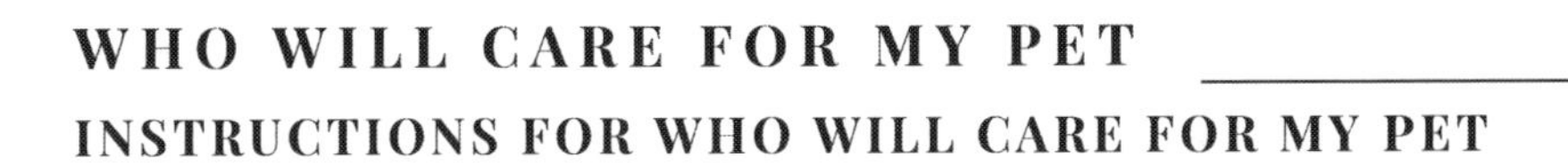

WHO WILL CARE FOR MY PET ______________________________

INSTRUCTIONS FOR WHO WILL CARE FOR MY PET

NAME	
DOB	
AGE	
GENDER	
BREED	
LICENSE	
NOTES:	

VET INFO

NAME	**WEBSITE**
ADDRESS	
PHONE	
EMAIL	

HEALTH INFO

MEDICINES
ALLERGIES

14. PETS' INFORMATION

WHO WILL CARE FOR MY PET ____________________

INSTRUCTIONS FOR WHO WILL CARE FOR MY PET

	NAME
	DOB
	AGE
	GENDER
	BREED
	LICENSE
	NOTES:

VET INFO

NAME	WEBSITE
ADDRESS	
PHONE	
EMAIL	

HEALTH INFO

MEDICINES
ALLERGIES

more notes

JAN	FEB	MAR	APR	MAY	JUN	JUL	AUG	SEP	OCT	NOV	DEC

1 2 3 4 5 6 7 8 9 10 11 12 13 14 15 16 17 18 19 20 21 22 23 24 25 26 27 28 29 30 31

15. Funeral Plans

15. FUNERAL PLANS

There are many ways to prepare for this ahead of time. Make sure that your loved ones have that Information. I have had several clients pay all the funeral expenses only to find out that their loved ones had prepaid for them but never told them. Big surprise, they don't get refunds.

Funeral/Burial Insurance Information

Contact Information

How I would prefer my remains to be cared for

Obituary Information I would like included

Notes

more notes

JAN	FEB	MAR	APR	MAY	JUN	JUL	AUG	SEP	OCT	NOV	DEC

1 2 3 4 5 6 7 8 9 10 11 12 13 14 15 16 17 18 19 20 21 22 23 24 25 26 27 28 29 30 31

16. Where is the important stuff

16. WHERE ARE ALL THE IMPORTANT DOCUMENTS

Making sure your heirs, beneficiaries, and people responsible know where to find this Information. I also suggest someplace they can access it easily. A safety deposit box is nice but if they aren't an authorized user, they will have to get a Court order to get access before they can even see what you have. Add them on as an authorized user ahead of time or make sure they have a copy of the key to prevent this from happening.

Estate Planning Documents

Driver's License-

Passport

Social Security Card

Birth Certificate

Marriage Certificate/Divorce Papers

Health Insurance Card

POA

Credit Cards

Bank Cards

Rewards Cards

Safety deposit box

Tax records

Mortgage Information

Car Loans

Student Loan

Medical Bills

Assets

Personal Loans

Judgments

more notes

JAN	FEB	MAR	APR	MAY	JUN	JUL	AUG	SEP	OCT	NOV	DEC

1 2 3 4 5 6 7 8 9 10 11 12 13 14 15 16 17 18 19 20 21 22 23 24 25 26 27 28 29 30 31

17. My Stuff

17. MY STUFF

This is one of the most important sections. I often hear people trying to resolve estates say that the person who passed doesn't have anything. That may be true, or more possibly, they just don't know what was of value to you. Make sure you list all belongings important to you and tell your loved ones how to get access to them and whom they should go to.

Real Estate

Address ________________

Co-Owners ________________

Mortgage Information ________________

Where is the document ________________

Appliance Information ________________

Security Information ________________

Commercial ________________

Address ________________

Co-Owners ________________

Where is the document ________________

Vehicles ________________

Make/Model/Year/Color ________________

VIN ________________

Loan/Lease Information ________________

Where is the document ________________

17. MY STUFF

Heirlooms and special things

Item

Location

Instructions

Safe

Location

Keys/Code

Firearms

Type

Registration Information

Location

Storage Units/Safety Deposit Box

Name and Location

Contact Information

Unit/Box #

Where are the keys

more notes

JAN	FEB	MAR	APR	MAY	JUN	JUL	AUG	SEP	OCT	NOV	DEC

1 2 3 4 5 6 7 8 9 10 11 12 13 14 15 16 17 18 19 20 21 22 23 24 25 26 27 28 29 30 31

18. Miscellaneous

To Do List

Day ______

Date & Month ______

No.	To Do	Yes/No

more notes

JAN	FEB	MAR	APR	MAY	JUN	JUL	AUG	SEP	OCT	NOV	DEC

1 2 3 4 5 6 7 8 9 10 11 12 13 14 15 16 17 18 19 20 21 22 23 24 25 26 27 28 29 30 31

19.
My
Thoughts

19. MY THOUGHTS

This book has been all business up to this point. This is an important section to speak to those you leave behind. Use this as an opportunity to say the things you always wished you had. Really, it's because you care.

NOTES

to those I love

MY NOTES TO:

date:

MY NOTES TO:

date:

MY NOTES TO:

date:

MY NOTES TO:

date:

MY NOTES TO:

date:

MY NOTES TO:

date:

MY NOTES TO:

date:

20. Glossary of Frequently Used Estate Terms

Glossary

Beneficiary/Heir

The persons who become the recipients of your estate.

Estate

The estate is the whole of the assets and debts you leave after you pass.

Executor

The person named in a Will to manage your estate after you pass.

Power of Attorney/POA

These documents are for while you are alive, but no longer able to care for yourself. They allow someone to make legal, medical, or financial decisions on your behalf.

Common Types of Power of Attorney Documents

Living Will/Health Care Directive or Medical Power of Attorney

Typically these are all documents you create that will allow someone to make medical and end-of-life decisions for you should you be unable.

HIPPA Waiver

This document will allow doctors to discuss your medical condition and needs with whomever you designate.

Durable Power of Attorney or Financial Power of Attorney

These documents allow someone to access your financial resources to care for your financial needs while you are alive but unable to care for yourself.

Glossary (Cont.)

Trust

A legally created entity that holds assets on behalf of the creator or Trustor. A trust can be revocable, meaning you can make changes to it, or irrevocable, meaning for the most part that you cannot make changes to it.

Trustor

The person or persons who create a trust.

Trustee

The persons who manage a trust.

Successor Trustees

The additional named persons who manage a trust.

Will

A legal document wherein you name your beneficiaries or heirs and designate what you want them to have.

more notes

JAN	FEB	MAR	APR	MAY	JUN	JUL	AUG	SEP	OCT	NOV	DEC

1 2 3 4 5 6 7 8 9 10 11 12 13 14 15 16 17 18 19 20 21 22 23 24 25 26 27 28 29 30 31

About the Author

Rena McDonald is the managing partner of McDonald Law Group and the Eclipse Law Group. Rena and her firms have been recognized for their achievements and have won many awards including Top 100 Lawyers, Best Business Firm in Henderson, Top 100 Women in Las Vegas, and are Best of Las Vegas award winners. Rena has also been featured in several magazines and identified as a "person to know" in Southern Nevada.

Rena McDonald is committed to serving the Las Vegas community. Rena was born and raised in Las Vegas and is very involved in improving our community. Rena was also recognized by the Henderson Chamber of Commerce and other organizations for her community service efforts.

Rena is a best-selling international author, entrepreneur, and mother.

NEED MORE HELP?

This book is not intended to be legal advice and does not replace a valid will, trust or estate plan. You should consult with a licensed attorney regarding any legal questions or concerns you may have. This book is for Informational purposes only.

For more information or questions please contact us at
www.eclipselawgroup.com

SHARE YOUR THOUGHTS

Thank you, Dear Reader,

If you have found this book useful
please share & leave a review
on Amazon **amzn.to/3XpkjIt**
and Goodreads.com

Scan the QR code

About the Publisher

Red Thread Publishing is an all-female publishing company on a mission to support 10,000 women to become successful published authors and thought leaders. Through the transformative work of writing & telling our stories, we are not only changed as individuals, but we are also changing the global narrative & thus the world.

www.redthreadbooks.com

facebook.com/redthreadpublishing
instagram.com/redthreadbooks

Made in the USA
Las Vegas, NV
13 December 2023